D1093949

RodandStaffBooks.com   800-761-0234
Grade 1 Pathway "More Days Go By" Reader

1098:ITEM #2-160

MORE
DAYS
GO BY

—illustrated by Lin Souliere
London, Ontario

Pathway Publishers
Aylmer, Ontario - LaGrange, Indiana

PATHWAY READING SERIES

FIRST STEPS, 140 pages	Grade 1
DAYS GO BY, 158 pages	Grade 1
MORE DAYS GO BY, 170 pages	Grade 1
BUSY TIMES, 249 pages	Grade 2
MORE BUSY TIMES, 288 pages	Grade 2
CLIMBING HIGHER, 248 pages	Grade 2
NEW FRIENDS, 284 pages	Grade 3
MORE NEW FRIENDS, 288 pages	Grade 3
BUILDING OUR LIVES, 496 pages	Grade 4
LIVING TOGETHER, 527 pages	Grade 5
STEP BY STEP, 416 pages	Grade 6
SEEKING TRUE VALUES, 464 pages	Grade 7
OUR HERITAGE, 478 pages	Grade 8

An accompanying workbook for this textbook is available from:

Pathway Publishers
2580N   250W
LaGrange, IN 46761

Printed in U.S.A.

CONTENTS

WINTER DAYS

HAPPY TIMES IN SPRING

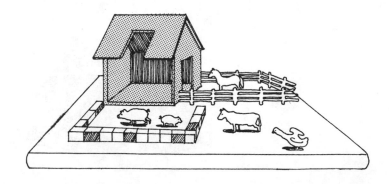

SIX YEARS OLD

"Happy Birthday!"

One morning Mother came into the house. Peter and Rachel were still in bed.

"Come, Peter," said Mother. "It is time to get up. You do not want to be late for school."

Peter jumped out of bed. He did not want to be late for school.

"Come here, Peter," said Mother. "I want to tell you something."

Peter ran to Mother. Mother said something to Peter. No one but Peter heard what Mother said.

Peter ran to Rachel's bed. "Happy birthday, Rachel!" he called. "Happy, happy birthday! Today is your birthday."

Rachel jumped up with a laugh.
"Yes, today is my birthday," she
said. "I am six years old now."
Rachel ran to Mother. Mother
said, "Good morning Rachel.
Good morning and happy birthday!"

Rachel smiled at Mother. She was very happy. She liked having a birthday.

Soon Dad and Mother and Peter and Rachel sat down to eat. Then Peter had to go to school.

"It is cold out this morning," said Mother. "Put on your coat and cap."

Peter put on his coat and cap. Then he went out the door. "Good by, Mother," he said.

"Good-by, Peter," said Mother. "Be a good boy in school today."

"I will try," said Peter. "Good-by, Rachel."

"Good-by, Peter," said Rachel. Then she went to the window. She saw Peter go to school.

"I am six years old now," said
Rachel. "I wish I could go to
school."

"You may go to school next
year," said Mother. "But you can
work for me now. That is what I
want you to do."

Rachel looked out the window again. She did not want to work. She did not want to play with Miriam. She wanted to go to school.

Rachel did not help Mother work. When Miriam cried, Rachel did not play with her. She just stood by the window and looked out.

Mother was not very happy with Rachel. She said, "You can not go to school now. You must learn to obey first. Little girls must obey in school. They must obey at home, too."

Rachel ran to help Mother. She still did not want to work. But she wanted to obey Mother. She wanted to be a good girl.

Grandfather and

Grandmother

Rachel helped Mother work.
She played with Miriam, too.
Soon Mother said, "You were a
big help, Rachel. You may go out
now if you want to. Andrew may
go, too."

"Good, good," said Rachel.
"Here is your coat and cap,
Andrew. We want to go out to the
barn."

Dad was working in the barn.
Rover was in the barn, too.
Rachel helped Dad work. Andrew
played with Rover.

Soon Dad did not have work for
Rachel. Then she played with
Blackie and the other kittens.
Rachel and Andrew stayed in the
barn all morning.

Then Rachel heard something.
"I hear a buggy," she said, as she
ran to the barn door. She saw a
buggy and a white horse.

"Grandfather and Grandmother
are coming," called Rachel.
"Come, Andrew. Grandfather and
Grandmother will want to see
you."

"Hello, Rachel," said Grandfather. "Hello, Andrew. I see Dad has help this morning. Soon Dad will not have to work. You will do all the work for him."

Rachel laughed. She liked Grandfather. "I can help Dad work," she said. "But I can not do all his work."

Rachel ran to the house. Grandmother went to the house, too. But she did not run. Oh, my, no! She was much too old to run.

"Surprise! Surprise!" called Rachel to Mother. "Grandfather and Grandmother are here. Did you know that?"

Mother came to the door. "No, I did not know that," she said. "What a happy surprise!"

Grandmother came into the house. She had a box in her hand. "Here, Rachel," said Grandmother. "Here is something for your birthday."

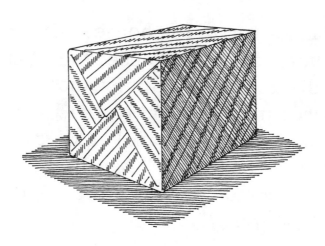

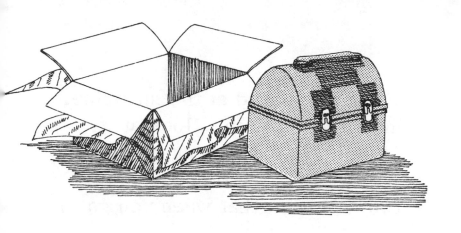

"Oh, thank you, " said Rachel. "May I open it? I want to see what is in this box. "

"Yes, you may open it, " said Grandmother.

Rachel opened the box. Then she said, "Oh, look, Mother. Come and see what I got for my birthday. Thank you, Grandmother. I like this surprise very much. "

Mother looked at the surprise. She said, "You may look at it, Rachel. Dad will want to see it, too. Then we will put it away. You will want that when you go to school."

"I wish I could go to school now," said Rachel. "I am six years old and I have this nice birthday surprise. But I can not go to school."

Mother said, "Next year you may go to school."

Two More Surprises

Mother and Grandmother went to work. They got something ready to eat. Rachel helped, too.

Soon Mother said, "Run to the barn, Rachel. Tell Dad and Grandfather to come in. We are ready to eat."

Rachel obeyed. She ran to the barn. When she came back, she saw something on the table. It was a big white cake.

"Oh, Mother," said Rachel. "Where did you get this cake?"

"I made it this morning, Rachel," said Mother. "I made it when you and Andrew were in the barn. This is your birthday cake."

"Oh, thank you," said Rachel. She had a big, big smile. "I like this big white cake."

Soon everyone sat down at the table. They all had something to eat. Then they had some cake, too.

"I like this cake," said Rachel. "My cake is very good."

"Yes, it is," said Grandfather. "You made a very good cake, Rachel."

"No, no, I did not make it,"
said Rachel. "Mother made it."

Grandfather looked surprised.
"What? You did not make this
cake? You said it was your cake."

"It is my cake," said Rachel.
"Mother made it for me. This is
my birthday cake."

"Oh, I see," said Grandfather.
"This is your cake. Mother made
it for you. It is a good cake."

That afternoon Grandmother
helped Mother work. Rachel
helped, too. But she was not very
happy. She did not want to work.
Soon she said, "Mother, may I go
home with Grandmother? May I
sleep at Grandmother's house? I
want to sleep there three nights."

Mother looked at Rachel. "Who will help me work?" she said. "Who will play with Miriam?"

"Andrew and Peter can help you work, Mother," said Rachel. "They can play with Miriam, too. I want to go home with Grandmother. Please, Mother, please."

"I do not know what to say," said Mother. "You want to go home with Grandmother. I want you here at home. What can we do?"

Just then Dad came into the house. Rachel said, "Please, Dad, may I go home with Grandmother? I want to sleep there three nights. May I, Dad? May I go?"

Dad looked at Mother and Mother looked at Dad. Soon Mother said, "Yes, Rachel, you may go home with Grandmother. But you must be a good girl and help Grandmother work."

"I will. I will," said Rachel. She jumped up and down. Then she ran to get ready. She was so happy to be going to Grandmother's house.

At Grandfather's House

Late that afternoon Rachel was
ready to go home with Grandfather and Grandmother. She
said, "I will work for Grandmother. But she does not have
much work. I will have time to
play, too. I will play all by
myself. I will do just what I want
to do."

Grandfather and Grandmother were on the buggy. They were ready to go home. Rachel was on the buggy, too. "Good-by, Mother. Good-by, Dad," she said.

"Good-by, Rachel," said Mother. "Be a good girl. You have to obey Grandmother."

"I will," said Rachel.

"Do not cry when it is time to go to bed," said Dad.

"I will not cry," said Rachel. "I am six years old now. I am a big girl."

Away went the horse and buggy. Away went Grandfather and Grandmother. And away went Rachel. Away she went to Grandfather's house.

Soon Grandfather and Grandmother and Rachel came to
Grandfather's house. Grandfather
went to put the horse in the barn.
Grandmother and Rachel went into
the house.

How still the house was! No
one was working in it. No boys
and girls were playing in it. No
baby was crying. The house was
very, very still.

Grandmother and Rachel went right to work. The house was not so still now. When there was no more work for Rachel to do, she went out to the barn. She ran with Grandfather as he did his work.

Then Grandfather and Grandmother and Rachel had something to eat. Soon Grandmother said, "I have a girl to help me work tonight. I do not have to do the work all by myself."
Rachel laughed. "I will help you, Grandmother." She worked fast.
Then Grandmother said, "What do you want to do now, Rachel? I do not have any work for you."

"I want to play, Grandmother, " said Rachel. "I know where the games are. May I play with them?"

"Yes, you may, " said Grandmother. "You may play with any game you want. "

Grandmother sat down. Rachel got a game and started to play with it. She said, "I wish Peter were here to help me play. He likes this game. "

"Peter is not here to help you,"
said Grandmother. "You must
play by yourself."

Rachel played a little. Then
she looked up. Grandmother was
sleeping. Grandfather was still
in the barn. The house was very,
very still.

Rachel **did** not like a house that
was very still. She wanted to cry.
But she said, "I am six years old.
I must not cry. I am too big to
cry."

Just then Grandfather came in.
He helped Rachel play a game.
The house was not so still now.

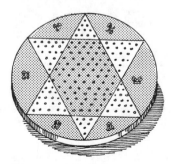

Soon Grandfather said, "It is time to go to bed. Can you sleep if you are not at home?"

"Oh, yes," said Rachel. "I can sleep at your house. I am going to stay here three nights."

Rachel said good-night to Grandfather and Grandmother and went to bed. But she could not sleep.

The house was very, very still
again. Rachel did not like this
house. She wanted to go home.
Rachel started to cry.
Grandmother was sleeping.
She did not hear Rachel cry.
Grandfather was sleeping, too.
He did not hear Rachel cry.
Rachel did not cry much. She
just cried a little. Then she went
to sleep.

A Day with Grandmother

The sun was up the next
morning when Rachel got out of
bed. She ran to Grandmother.
"Good morning, " she said.

"Good morning, Rachel, " said
Grandmother. "Did you have a
good sleep?"

Rachel said, "I could not go to
sleep last night. But I had a good
sleep."

Rachel had something to eat.
Then she said, "What can I do for
you, Grandmother?"

Grandmother said, "I do not
have any work for you this
morning. You may play if you
want to."

"Good," said Rachel. "Today
I can do just what I want to do. I
do not have to work for Mother.
I do not have to play with Miriam.
I will play all by myself. And
I will have a good time."

Rachel played with one game.
Then she put it away and played
with another game. She played
with three games. She played with
Grandmother's doll and doll bed,
too. By and by Rachel said,
"May I go out, Grandmother? I
want to be with Grandfather."

Grandmother said, "I am sorry, Rachel, but Grandfather is not at home. He went away this morning when you were still in bed."

"When will he come home?" asked Rachel.

"He will come home tonight," said Grandmother. "But you may go out if you want to. You may look at all the animals in the barn."

Rachel put on her coat and went outside. Soon she came back in. "I want something to do, Grandmother," she said.

"Here are the games, Rachel," said Grandmother. "Do you want to play with them?"

Rachel said, "I do not like to play all by myself. I wish Peter and Andrew were here to play with me."

"Peter and Andrew are not here," said Grandmother. "So they can not play with you."

Grandmother sat on her chair and worked. Rachel sat on her chair and played. The house was still again. It was very, very still.

Rachel did not want to stay at Grandmother's house. She did not want to play all by herself. She started to cry. "I want to go home," she said. "I want to go home right now."

Grandmother looked surprised. "Do you want to go home?" she said. "You wanted to sleep here three nights."

"Yes, I wanted to sleep here three nights," said Rachel. "But I do not want to stay here now. I want to go home. Please, Grandmother. May I go home now?"

"I am going to the store this afternoon," said Grandmother. "I will take you home then if you want to go."

"Oh, I do. I do," said Rachel. She was happy now. She was happy to know she was going home.

Home Again

Grandmother and Rachel had something to eat. Then Grandmother got ready to go to the store. Rachel got ready to go home.

Grandmother said, "Do you want to go to the store with me, Rachel? We can go to the store first. Then I will take you home."

Rachel said, "I like going to the store, Grandmother. But I do not want to go to the store this afternoon. I want to go home."

"All right," said Grandmother. "If you do not want to go to the store, then I will take you home first."

Soon Grandmother and Rachel were going down the road. Grandmother said, "Your mother will be surprised to see you, Rachel. You said you were going to sleep at our house three nights. Mother will not be looking for you today."

"Mother will be happy to see me," said Rachel. "She has work for me to do. She will want me to play with Miriam, too."

"Did you like to sleep at our house?" asked Grandmother.

Rachel looked down. She said, "Your house is too still, Grandmother. And I do not like to play by myself. At home I can play with Peter and Andrew and Miriam. At your house I do not have anyone to play with."

Grandmother did not say anything. She just smiled.

Soon Rachel said, "I see our
barn, Grandmother. And there
is Dad. I see him, Grandmother!
I see Dad!"

Rachel jumped from the buggy
as soon as Grandmother stopped.
"Hello, Dad," she said. "Grandmother is going to the store. I
am not going with her. I am going
to stay here."

"Good," said Dad. "I am glad
to hear that. Andrew will be
glad, too. He wanted you, Rachel.
He wanted to play with you. "
    "I wanted to play with Andrew,
too, " said Rachel. "I do not want
to sleep at Grandfather's house
three nights. I want to stay at
home. "

    That day Rachel helped Mother
work. She played with Miriam.
She said, "I like this house.
Grandmother's house is too still.
No boys and girls are playing in it.
No baby is crying in it. I did not
like playing by myself. "
    "I am glad you came home,
Rachel, " said Mother.
    "I am, too, " said Rachel. "I
am glad to be at home— very,
very glad. "

IN GRADE ONE

A Funny Animal

It was a pretty morning. The
sun was out and the sky was very,
very blue. The trees were not
green now. They were yellow and
orange and red and brown.

Peter and Levi were walking to
school. Peter did not have on his
coat and cap. He just had on his
hat.

When Peter and Levi walked to
school, they went by Mr. Brown's
farm. Mr. Brown lived all by
himself in a little green house.
He did not have a big farm.

Peter and Levi liked Mr. Brown.
They liked to stop and talk to him.

Mr. Brown liked animals.
Many, many animals lived on his
little farm.

This morning Peter and Levi
did not see Mr. Brown. But they
saw something in his field. It was
an animal that looked a little like
a horse. It was little and gray.
It had big, big ears.

Peter saw the animal first. He said, "Look, Levi! What is that animal? It looks a little like a horse, but it is not a horse."

Levi looked and looked at the animal. "I do not know what it is," he said. "But I know it is not a horse. Horses do not have big ears like that."

Just then the animal saw Peter
and Levi. Up went the animal's
head. Out went its tail, and down
went one big ear. "Hee-haw!
Hee-haw!" cried the animal.

Peter and Levi laughed. Peter
said, "I do not know what that
animal is. But I know one thing.
It is a funny animal with a funny
cry."

"Yes, it is," said Levi. "But
we can not stay here and look at
the animal all day. We have to
go now. We do not want to be
late for school."

Peter and Levi went to school.
They ran all the way. When they
got there, a big boy came out of
the schoolhouse.

Levi said, "We saw a funny
animal in Mr. Brown's field this
morning. It looked a little like
a horse, but it was not as big as
a horse."

"It had big ears and a funny
cry," said Peter.

The boy laughed. "You saw
Mr. Brown's donkey," he said.
"I saw it, too, when I came to
school."

Peter and Levi ran to find the
other little boys. They wanted to
tell them about the donkey.

Peter told the other boys about
the donkey's big ears. Levi told
them about his funny head and tail.
The boys told about the donkey's
funny cry, too.

Soon all the little boys in school
were crying like a donkey.
"Hee-haw!" they said. "Hee-haw!
Hee-haw! Hee-haw!"

Something to Laugh At

Soon Peter and Levi and the other boys heard the bell. Everyone ran into the schoolhouse. It was time for school to start.

Peter went into the schoolhouse, too. He was not thinking about school. He was thinking about the donkey that had come to live with Mr. Brown.

Peter went to his seat and sat down. The other boys and girls sat down, too.

Then Peter heard a girl laugh. He looked around to see what she was laughing at. By then more girls were laughing. The boys were laughing, too.

Peter still could not see what was funny. He looked all around. He wanted to laugh, too.

Then Peter saw that everyone was looking at him. Everyone was looking at him and laughing. Peter did not like that. He did not want the other boys and girls to laugh at him.

Teacher Dan saw what was funny. He wanted to help Peter. He said, "Did you forget something, Peter?"

Peter tried to think. What did he forget? But Peter could not think at all. He could not think when everyone was laughing at him.

Teacher Dan tried again. He said, "Put your hand on your head, Peter. You did forget something."

Up went Peter's hand. He wanted to put it on his head. But he could not do that. His hat was in the way.

Now Peter knew what was funny. He knew what the boys and girls were laughing at. He was in school with his hat on.

Peter took off his hat. He took
it off fast. But he did not know
what to do with it. He looked at
Teacher Dan.
"Put your hat away, Peter," said
Teacher Dan. "Go and put it
away, then come back to your
seat again."

Peter went out of the room. He
put his hat away. But he did not
come back in. "The others will
laugh at me again," he said to
himself. "I will not like that."
Peter did not want to stay out
of the room. He did not want to
go back in. He did not know what
to do. Peter started to cry.

Teacher Dan came to Peter.
"Do not cry, Peter," he said. "Be
a big boy and come back to your
seat."

"You all laughed at me," said
Peter. "I did not like that."

"We did not laugh at you," said
Teacher Dan. "We just laughed
at the funny thing you did. We all
do funny things. We have to learn
to laugh at the funny things we do."

Peter did not cry now. But he could not laugh. His face was still very red. He went back to his seat.

Peter did not look around at all. He just looked down at his book. He did not hear anyone laugh. "I do not think it is funny to forget something," Peter said to himself. "I do not like to have the others laugh at me. I will not laugh at others when they do something funny."

Laughing at Levi

That very same day Levi did something funny, too. The boys and girls in Grade One did not have anything to do. They could not sit still.

Teacher Dan looked at the little boys and girls. Then he said, "You want something to do. I have a picture for you to color. Will you like that?"

"Yes, yes," said all the boys and girls. They liked to color pictures.

Here is the farm.

Teacher Dan gave them a
picture to color. Then he said,
"What do you see in the picture,
Peter?"

Peter said, "I see a barn and a
tree. I see a cow, too."

"Very good," said Teacher Dan.
"What color will you make the
things in this picture, Levi?"

Levi said, "I will make the barn
red and the tree green and brown.
I will make the cow black and
white."

A little girl said, "I will make the sky blue and white."

"Very good," said Teacher Dan. "Now you have something to do. Do not work too fast. I want to see pretty pictures when you are done."

The children in Grade One went to work. Levi worked fast. He wanted to be done first.

Levi colored the barn red. He colored the sky blue and white. Then he colored the tree green.

Levi did not think about what he was doing. He was thinking about getting done first. Levi did not color the cow black and white. He colored it green.

Just then Peter looked up from his work. He saw the green cow in Levi's picture. The green cow looked very funny. Peter started to laugh.

Everyone looked at Peter. They wanted to see what was funny. Then they saw Levi's picture. They saw the green cow, too. They knew what was funny now. Soon everyone in the room was laughing.

At first Levi did not know what was funny. He looked at his picture. Then he saw the green cow. "Oh, oh!" he said. "I was not thinking when I colored that cow."

Levi's face got very red, but he did not cry. He just laughed with the other children.

Teacher Dan came and looked at Levi's picture. He had to laugh, too. Teacher Dan said, "You worked too fast, Levi. You did not think about what you were doing. You will have to start over. I will give you a new picture."

Levi took the new picture. He
did not work so fast now. He did
not color the cow green. He
colored it black and white.

Peter was done with his picture.
He was not working. He was
thinking about Levi and his funny
green cow.

"I did not want to laugh at Levi," thought Peter. "But his picture looked so funny, I had to laugh. Levi did not cry when we laughed at him. He just laughed, too."

Then Peter thought, "The next time I do something funny, I will not cry. I will laugh at myself."

Something for the Donkey

The next morning Peter and
Levi walked to school again. "Do
you think that donkey will be in
Mr. Brown's field?" asked Levi.

"I hope so, " said Peter. "The donkey is not very pretty, but I like to look at him. I hope it will be in the field every day. "

When the boys got to Mr. Brown's farm, they saw the donkey. As soon as the donkey saw the boys, his head went up. Out went his tail and down went one big ear. "Hee-haw! Hee-haw!" cried the donkey.

The donkey started to run. He ran right up to the fence where the boys stood. He put his head over the fence. "Hee-haw!" he said again.

"The donkey wants something, " said Levi. "He wants something to eat. I wish I had something for him. "

Peter started to think. "I may have something, " he said. He opened his dinner bucket to see what he had. "Here is just the thing, " he said. "The donkey will like this big red apple. "

"Yes, he will, " said Levi. "Dad told me donkeys like apples. "

Peter looked at the apple in his hand. Then he looked at the donkey. "Do you think the donkey will bite?" he asked. "Do you think he will bite my hand if I give him this apple?"

"I hope not, but I do not know," said Levi. "I like to give our horses apples. They do not bite. But I do not know about this donkey. I do not know if he will bite or not."

Peter wanted the donkey to have the apple. But he did not want him to take it from his hand.

By this time the donkey had seen the apple. He had seen the apple, and he wanted it. He ran up and down on the other side of the fence. It looked as if the donkey wanted to say, "Hurry up and give me that apple."

Peter put the apple by the fence and ran away. He looked back to see if the donkey had found the apple.

The donkey ran up to the apple.
He took a big bite. He ate that
bite in a hurry. Then he took one
more bite.

"Look, Levi," said Peter.
"The donkey liked my apple. Did
you see how fast he ate it?"

"Yes, I did," said Levi. "But
now we have to hurry fast, too.
If we do not hurry, we will be
late for school. Teacher Dan will
not like that."

Mr. Brown and Shag

A week went by. Every morning when Peter and Levi walked to school, they saw the donkey. Every morning the donkey came running up to the fence. Every morning Peter had an apple for the donkey.

One morning Mr. Brown came walking up the road. He saw Peter put an apple by the fence. He saw the donkey eat the apple.

"Good morning, boys, " said Mr. Brown. He had a big smile on his face. "What do you think of Shag by this time?" he asked.

"Shag?" said Levi. "Who is Shag?"

Mr. Brown laughed. "Can you
guess who Shag is?" he asked.
"Shag is my friend, and by the
looks of things, he is your friend,
too. Shag likes apples, and he
likes boys who give him apples."

"Now I know," laughed Peter. "This donkey's name is Shag. Am I right about that?"

"Yes, you are," said Mr. Brown. "What do you think of him?"

"We like him," said Levi. "He comes up to the fence every morning."

"I have seen him come up to the fence," said Mr. Brown. "I have seen you give him apples, too. Someday Shag will have to give you a ride. He will have to give you a ride for all the apples you are giving him."

"Oh, oh," said Peter and Levi at the same time. "We want a ride now."

"No, no, not today," said Mr.
Brown. "I do not have time today.
And Shag is not ready to give
children rides now. Someday he
will— someday when I have time
to help you."

"Will Shag bite?" asked Peter.
"I do not let him take apples from
my hand. I do not want him to
bite me."

"Oh, no, Shag will not bite,"
said Mr. Brown. He walked up
and put his hand on the donkey's
head. "Shag is a good donkey.
He will not bite."

From then on Peter and Levi
talked and talked about Shag.
They talked about him at school
and at home. They talked about
the ride Shag was going to give
them.

That night Mother heard Peter
talk about Shag. She heard him
talk about the apples he gave to
Shag.

"Apples?" she said. "Where
do you get the apples you give to
Shag?"

"In my dinner bucket, Mother, "
said Peter. "I let Shag eat the
apples you put in my dinner
bucket for me. "
Mother was not very happy.
"I did not put the apples into your
dinner bucket for Shag, " she said.
"I put them there for you. "
"But Shag likes apples,
Mother, " said Peter. "Mr.
Brown said he likes apples and
boys who give him apples. I
want that donkey to like me,
Mother. "

Dad heard what Peter said.
"Shag will like corn, too, " he
said. "You may take an ear of
corn for the donkey every
morning. Then you can eat the
apples and Shag can eat the corn. "
    Peter looked happy now. "That
is just what I will do, " he said.
"I will take an ear of corn for
Shag every morning. I hope Shag
will like the corn. "

Levi's Surprise

The next morning when Peter went to school he had an ear of corn in one hand. He had his dinner bucket in the other hand.

Peter thought, "I will put the corn into the dinner bucket. Then I will not have to carry it in my hand."

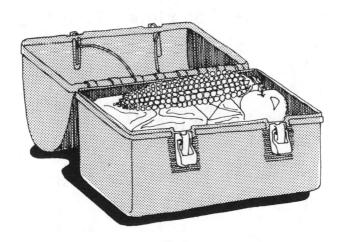

That is just what Peter did. He
put the corn into his dinner
bucket. Then he ran up the road
to Levi's house.

Levi came running out of the
house. He was very happy about
something. "Guess what!" he
said. "Guess what our cow has!"

"She has a calf," guessed
Peter. "Is that right, Levi? Did
I guess right?"

"Yes, you did," said Levi.
"But she has more than one calf.
Our cow has twins!"

"Oh, oh," said Peter. "Do we
have time to look at the twins? I
want to see them."

"We have time if we hurry,"
said Levi. He and Peter ran to
the barn. There they saw the cow
with her two little calves.

Peter said, "I wish our cow had twin calves. I think your calves are very nice, Levi. But now we have to hurry. We do not want to be late this morning."

Peter and Levi walked up the road. Peter heard something. He looked around. "Here comes a buggy," he said.

The buggy came up to Peter and Levi. It stopped. The man in the buggy said, "Do you want a ride, boys? You may ride with me."

"Yes, we do," said Peter. "We will ride to school with you."

Soon Peter and Levi were sitting
on the buggy. Then down the road
they went. The man on the buggy
talked to the boys.

Soon the buggy came to the
schoolhouse. It stopped. Out
jumped Peter and Levi. "Thank
you for the ride," they said to
the man. Then they ran into the
schoolhouse.

Peter forgot all about Shag. He
forgot all about the corn in his
dinner bucket. He put his dinner
bucket away. Then he took off
his hat and put it away, too.
Soon Peter heard the bell. It
was time for school to start.
Peter went to his seat and sat
down. He was ready for a good
day at school.

Peter Laughs at Himself

That morning Peter did his
work. Then he made a picture of
a cow. He made two little calves
in the picture, too. He colored
the cow and the calves black and
white.

When it was time to play, Peter gave the picture to Levi. "This is for you," he said. "This is a picture of your cow and her twins."

Levi looked at the picture. "Thank you, Peter," he said. "I like this picture. I will take it home for Susan. She will like it, too."

Peter and Levi went out to play. Soon they heard the bell. Then they had to go back to their seats again.

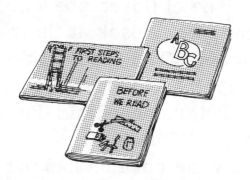

Teacher Dan had more work
for the children in Grade One.
They worked in their books. Then
they colored a picture of a horse
and her colt.

Soon Teacher Dan said, "Put
your books away. It is time to
eat."

Peter was glad to put his books
away. He was ready to eat.

"Go wash your hands and get
your dinner buckets," said
Teacher Dan.

The children obeyed. Soon
they were back at their seats
again. They opened their dinner
buckets and started to eat.

Peter opened his dinner bucket,
too. What did he see then? He
saw the corn he had put there for
Shag.

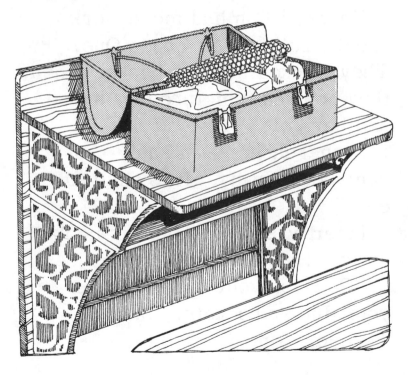

The other children saw the corn, too. Everyone started to laugh. Peter laughed, too.

When Peter could stop laughing, he said, "I put this corn in here for the donkey. I put it into the dinner bucket so I would not have to carry it in my hand. Then Levi told me about the twin calves in their barn. When we went to school, we had a ride in a buggy. I did not see Shag. I did not think of the corn in my dinner bucket. I forgot all about it."

Everyone in the room thought the corn in Peter's dinner bucket was funny. They laughed and laughed.

By and by Teacher Dan said, "Put the corn away, Peter. It is time to eat now. You can give the corn to Shag on the way home."

"I will do that," said Peter. "But tomorrow morning I will not put Shag's corn into my dinner bucket. I will carry it in my hand. Then I will not forget about it."

The other children stopped laughing. They started to eat. Peter ate his dinner, too. All the time he was eating, he was thinking. "I did not cry when the other boys and girls laughed at me," he thought. "I just laughed with them. I laughed at myself."

WINTER DAYS

"Winter Is Here!"

One morning when Rachel got out of bed, Mother said, "Come to the window, Rachel. Winter is here!"

Rachel ran to the window. "Oh, it snowed last night," she said. She jumped up and down. "I like snow. Everything looks so pretty."

Rachel looked at the snow. Then she looked at Mother. "May I call Peter and Andrew?" she asked. "They will want to see the snow, too."

"No, we will let them sleep as long as they want to," said Mother. "Today is not a school day. Peter will not have to get up early this morning."

"I saw the snow first," said
Rachel. "I will tell Peter that
when he gets up."

Just then Dad came in the door.
He heard what Rachel said. "Oh,
no, you did not see the snow
first," he laughed. "Mother and
I saw it before you did."

"I saw it before Peter and Andrew did," said Rachel. "Is the snow very deep, Dad?"

"No, it is not very deep," said Dad. "And it is not very cold outside. The snow will be just right to make a snowman."

"Good, good," said Rachel. "I like to make a snowman. Peter likes it, too. I hope he will not sleep too long. If he does, I will make a snowman before he gets up."

Just then Peter walked into the kitchen. He still looked very sleepy.

"Oh, Peter," said Rachel.
"Come and look at the snow.
Winter is here."

Peter was not sleepy now. He
ran to the window and looked out.

Rachel said, "The snow is not
very deep, Peter. Dad said it is
just right to make a snowman."

"May we go out and make a
snowman right now?" asked Peter.
"Please, Mother, may we?"

"Oh, my, no!" said Mother.
"We want to eat breakfast first.
You must have a good breakfast
before you go out."

Soon Dad and Mother and Peter
and Rachel sat down to eat
breakfast. Andrew and Miriam
were not in the kitchen. They
were still in bed.

When everyone was done eating,
Dad said, "This is the first snow
of the winter. I know Peter and
Rachel want to play in it. Mother
and I will do the work. The
children may play in the snow."

"Oh, thank you! Thank you!"
said Rachel. She had a happy
look on her face.

"Thank you! Thank you!" said
Peter. He ran to get his coat and
cap.

"Put on your new mittens," said Mother. "Your hands will get cold."

Soon Peter and Rachel were ready to go. They had on big coats. They had on their new mittens, too.

Then the two children ran out the door. Out they ran into the pretty white snow.

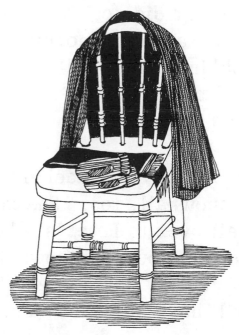

The Snow Family

Rachel stood and looked at the
snow. It was very, very white.
The sky was very blue, and the
sun was out.

"What a pretty morning," said
Rachel. "I like winter mornings
like this."

Peter did not have time to talk
about a pretty morning. He was
making a snowball. He rolled
and rolled the snowball. Soon it
was very big.

By this time Rachel was making
a snowball, too. She rolled her
ball over to Peter's. "Come and
help me put my snowball on top
of yours," she called. "Then we
will have our snowman."

Peter came to help Rachel.
Then he said, "I will get some
eyes for this snowman. Will you
get a nose for him?"

"Yes, I will," said Rachel. "I
know just what we want for a
nose."

Soon the snowman had eyes and a nose. He had a mouth, too. "I know where Dad's old hat is," said Rachel. "That old hat will look funny on our snowman."

Rachel ran to get the old hat. When she came back, Peter was making another snowball.

"What are you doing now?" asked Rachel.

"I am making another snowman," said Peter. "This snowman will not be as big as the first one. It will be the snowman's little boy."

Rachel laughed. "That will be fun," she said. "We want to make a little girl, too."

"We can make a snow family," said Peter. "We will want a mother, too."

"Yes, and four children," said Rachel. She started to make another snowball, too.

Peter and Rachel played and
played. They had so much fun
with their snow family. Andrew
came out of the house and helped,
too. Before long the snow family
was done.

Peter said, "We want Dad and
Mother to see the snow family. I
will call Dad, Rachel. Will you
go to the house and tell Mother to
come out?"

Soon Dad came out of the barn
with Peter. At the same time
Mother came out of the house with
Rachel. They thought the snow
family was very funny.

Peter said, "I want to put the first letter of our names on the snow family. The big snowman will have Dad's first letter. The next one will have Mother's first letter. What can I use to make the letters?"

Dad thought a little. Then he said, "Corn will make nice letters, Peter. You can use corn to make the letters."

"Corn?" said Peter. "How can I make letters with corn?"

"Run and get an ear of corn, and I will help you start," said Dad.

Peter got the corn in a hurry.
Dad helped Peter get started, then
he went back to his work. Peter
made a letter on every snowman.
"Mother and Miriam start with
the same letter," he said. "But
the snow mother is big, and the
snow baby is little."

Soon there was no more work to do on the snow family. "I hope it will stay cold," said Peter. "If it gets warm, our snow family will melt. I will not like that."

"If this snow family melts, we will make a new family when it snows again," said Rachel.

"Yes, we will," said Peter. "We will have a snow family all winter."

Who Took the Corn?

The next morning Peter jumped
out of bed. He went to the window
and looked out. "Oh, good," he
thought. "The snow family did not
melt. I can still see it."

Just then Mother came in from the barn. "It is very cold this morning," she said. "It snowed a little more, too."

Peter said, "I looked out the window. The snow family did not melt. It is still there."

"Yes, it is still there," said Mother. "But we do not have time to talk about the snow family this morning. It will soon be time to go to church."

"Oh, good," said Peter. "I like to go to church. I will call Rachel and Andrew."

"Yes, please do," said Mother. She started to get breakfast ready.

Before long everyone was in the kitchen. The family sat down to eat breakfast. Then they worked fast to get ready to go to church.

When Peter came out of the house, he ran to look at the snow family. Rachel went with him.

"Oh, look," said Peter. "There is snow on the big snowman's hat."

"Yes, it snowed on all the snow family," said Rachel. "The little children look so cold."

"They want to be cold," laughed Peter. "They would melt if they were warm."

"Yes, I know," said Rachel. Then she and Peter ran out to the buggy. Soon the buggy was going down the road. The family was going to church.

When Peter and Rachel came home that day, they went into the house. Soon Peter went to the window and looked out. "Oh, oh!" he said. "Something happened to the snow family. Something happened to the letters I made. The corn is not there."

Rachel and Andrew came to the
window, too. "Someone took the
corn," said Rachel. "Who do you
think took it?"

"I think the corn melted," said
Andrew. "The snow family did not
melt, but the corn did."

"No, no, corn can not melt,"
said Peter. "I think something
ate it."

Just then the children saw
something. A bird came down and
sat on the snow baby. The bird
was blue and white. It was very
pretty.

"Oh, oh, oh!" said Rachel.
"Look at that pretty bird. Now we
know what happened to the corn.
Now we know who took it!"

"The bird did not eat all the corn," said Peter. "There is some on the ground. I can see it from here."

Just then two more birds came to eat corn. They sat on the ground and started to eat.

Mother came to the window. "The birds are hungry," she said. "When the ground is white with snow, they can not find anything to eat."

"I know three birds that found something to eat," said Peter. "They found the letters I made with corn."

Mother said, "We will ask Dad to make a bird feeder for us. Then the birds will have something to eat. We can watch the birds come to the feeder."

"Oh, I will like that," said Rachel. "I like to watch the birds. We will feed them every day. Then they will not be hungry."

The

Bird

Feeder

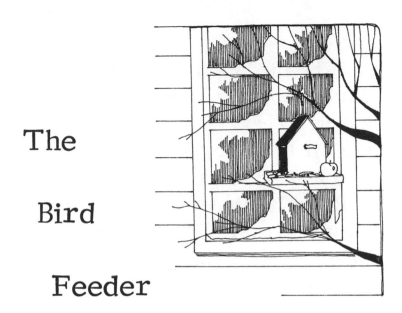

The very next day Dad made a bird feeder. Mother and Rachel put corn and seeds into it. They put in other feed, too.

Dad put the feeder on the tree outside the window. He put ears of corn on the fence, too.

"The birds will see the corn,"
said Rachel. "They will come to
eat it. They will eat the feed in
the bird feeder, too. Then they
will not be hungry."

Rachel watched and watched
for the birds. "When will the
birds come?" she asked again
and again.

Mother said, "Give them time,
Rachel. If they do not come
today, maybe they will come
tomorrow."

Rachel did not want to wait.
She wanted the birds to come to
the feeder now. She stood by the
window and watched and watched.

Andrew said, "Come, Rachel.
Come and help me play with my
little animals."

Rachel played with Andrew.
She forgot all about the bird
feeder. By and by Mother said,
"Look at the bird feeder now,
Rachel."

Rachel and Andrew ran to the window. "Oh, oh," said Rachel. "See the little gray and black birds. They have found our feeder."

The little birds saw Rachel and Andrew at the window. Away went the little birds. Rachel and Andrew could not see them any more.

"Oh, we made the birds fly away," said Rachel. "We did not want to do that."

Mother said, "They will come back again. They know where they can find something to eat now. They will come back again when they are hungry."

It was not long until the little
gray and black birds were back.
A pretty red bird came to the
feeder, too.

Rachel and Andrew stood by the
window and watched the birds.
They stood very still and did not
move. They did not want to make
the birds fly away again.

The Funny Bird

Days and weeks went by. It was still cold outside. The snow stayed on the ground.

On some days the sun was out, and it was not very cold. Some of the snow melted then. But soon more snow fell. Then everything was white and pretty again.

It was not long until many, many birds came to the feeder. There were little birds and big birds. There were gray and black birds and red birds. There were blue birds and brown birds, too.

Some of the birds sat in the feeder to eat. Other birds ate the feed that fell to the ground. The pretty red birds liked the corn Dad put on the fence.

The children liked to watch the birds in the feeder. Every day they watched to see if any new birds came to the feeder.

One morning Andrew went to the window. He saw something in the bird feeder. It was brown and had a big, big tail.

Andrew looked and looked. Then
he said, "Come here, Rachel.
Come and see what is in the bird
feeder. It is a funny bird."

Rachel came running to the
window. "Oh, oh," she said.
"That is not a bird. It is a
squirrel! Look, look, Mother! A
squirrel is sitting in the bird
feeder. It is eating the feed we
put out for the birds."

Mother came to the window.
She laughed. "I guess that
squirrel is hungry, too, " she
said. "It is getting a good
breakfast this morning. "

Just then Rachel saw a red bird
fly up to the feeder. It sat on the
tree not far from the feeder.

Up went the squirrel's head. It
was not eating now. It started to
bark at the bird. Up and down
went the squirrel's big tail. How
funny it looked! Mother and the
children laughed and laughed.

Soon the squirrel went away.
But the next day it came back.
Every day Rachel and Andrew saw
the squirrel.

Sometimes the squirrel did not
come up to the bird feeder.
Sometimes it just ate the corn on
the fence.

Rachel liked to watch the
squirrel, but she liked the birds
better. "We want to feed the birds
all year," she said.

Mother said, "The birds will not come to the feeder when there is no snow on the ground. Then they can find food in the fields. But when it snows, they can not find food in the fields. They get hungry then. When they are hungry, they fly around looking for food. That is how they happened to find our feeder."

"I am glad we have this feeder," said Rachel. "I do not want the birds to be hungry."

The Toy Farm

Andrew had many toy animals. He had two mother pigs and some little pigs. He had cows and calves and sheep and goats. He had chickens and donkeys, too. And he had one toy dog.

Andrew liked to play with his toy animals. Every day he took them out of the box and played with them.

"I wish I had a barn," said Andrew. "I do not want a big barn— just a little toy barn for my animals."

"Maybe Dad will make a barn for you," said Rachel. "He made a little house for me. He could make a barn, too."

Andrew ran to find Dad. "I wish I had a barn," he said. "Please, Dad, will you make a barn for me?"

"A barn?" said Dad. He looked surprised. "We have a barn, Andrew. What would we want with another barn?"

"No, no, I do not want a big barn," said Andrew. "Just a little toy barn for my animals. Will you make one for me?"

Dad laughed, "Oh, now I see," he said. "You do not want a big barn. You just want a toy barn." He thought a little, then he said, "Yes, Andrew. I think I can make just the barn you want. But I can not do it today. I have other work to do."

Andrew was very happy. He ran back to the house to play with his animals. He made a big pen with his toy fence. "This pen is for the horses," he said. "I will make a pen for the cows, too. And I will make a little pen for the ducks and chickens. They can all be in one pen."

That is just what Andrew did.
He made pens for all his animals.
He did not have fence for all the
pens. He made some of the pens
with his blocks.

The next morning Andrew asked,
"Do you have time to make my toy
barn today, Dad?"
Dad said, "I am sorry, Andrew.
I do not have time today. I have
to go help a man work. I will
make your barn some other day."

All that day Andrew played with his animals. He played with his toy fence and blocks. He liked to play with all his toys, but he wished he had a barn. Oh, how he wished for a barn!

That night Andrew was playing with his toys again. Dad came into the room. He watched Andrew play.

"Look at my farm," said Andrew. "I have a pen for my horses and a pen for my cows. I have pens for all the other animals, too. But I do not have a barn on my farm."

"What?" said Dad. "A farm
without a barn? That will not do.
I will make a barn for your farm,
Andrew. I will take time to do it
tomorrow."

Andrew was very happy. He
jumped up and down. "I will help
you make a barn, Dad," he said.
"It will not take long if I help you."

The New Toy Barn

The next morning Dad said, "Today we will make your barn, Andrew. We will make it in the shop. Do you want to help?"

"Yes, I do," said Andrew. He ran to get his coat and cap.

Soon Dad and Andrew were in the shop. Dad got his saw and some wood. He got his hammer, too.

Andrew saw the wood. He said, "This wood is brown. I do not want a brown barn, Dad. I want a red barn."

Dad laughed a little. He said, "Yes, this wood is brown. We will make a brown barn. Then we will paint it. You will have a red barn, Andrew."

Andrew was very happy. "I will
have a red barn," he said. "That
is just what I want."

Dad worked on the barn. He
used his saw and his hammer.
Soon Andrew had a little toy barn.

"This is just the barn I
wanted," said Andrew. "I want
to play with it right now."

Dad said, "You can not play with the barn now, Andrew. I want to paint it first. I will find some paint and do it right now."

Dad found the paint. It did not take him long to paint the little barn. Andrew watched Dad paint the barn red. Soon it was not a brown barn. It was red all over.

Dad went to put the paint away. Andrew thought, "I will take this barn in now. I can carry it. I want to put my animals into it."

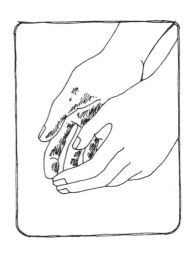

Dad saw Andrew take the barn.
"No, no, Andrew," he said.

But it was too late. Some red
paint was on Andrew's hands. His
coat was red, too.

"Look at your hands, Andrew,"
said Dad. "Look at your coat,
too. Mother will not like that."

Andrew looked at his hands and
coat. He did not look happy. "I
wanted to carry the toy barn to the
house," he said. "I wanted to
play with it."

"Oh, no, you can not play with the barn today," said Dad. "The paint is still wet. It will not be dry until tomorrow."

"May I play with the barn tomorrow?" asked Andrew.

"Tomorrow I will give it another coat of paint," said Dad. "Then it will be wet again. By the next day the paint will be dry. Then you may play with it."

Andrew did not want to wait two days to play with his new barn. But he could not play with it now—not when the paint was still wet. All he could do was wait.

Miriam and the Toy Barn

At last the day came when
Andrew could play with the toy
barn. He put it on the floor and
made a fence around one side.
"My cows can go here," he said.
"The horses will go into the barn."

Soon all the toy animals were on
the floor, too. Andrew played and
played with his toy farm. He put
the animals into the barn. Then
he took them out again.

Andrew used his fence and his blocks to make pens for all the animals. He said, "This goat will run at all the other animals. I will make a pen just for him."

Andrew made a pen for the goat. Then he made one for all the other animals but the dog. "My dog does not have to be in a pen," he said. "He may run all over my farm."

Rachel was in the same room
with Andrew. Soon she said,
"Oh, Andrew. Come to the
window. I see a new bird at the
feeder. I have not seen a bird
like this before."

Andrew ran to the window. He
saw a big black and white bird.
The top of its head was red. "Oh,
what a pretty bird," said Andrew.

Miriam was on the floor. She saw the toy barn and all the toy animals. She wanted to play, too.

Miriam went to the toy barn. Andrew did not see her there. But soon he heard something. He looked around to see what was going on.

"NO! NO! NO!" cried Andrew. He came running as fast as he could run. But it was too late. Down went all the fences. Down went many of the animals. Andrew did not have a nice farm now.

Andrew was not happy at all. "Go away, Miriam," he said. "You may not play with this farm. It is my farm!"

Miriam started to cry. Mother heard Miriam cry. She had heard what Andrew said, too.

"Andrew, Andrew," said Mother. "You have to be nice to Miriam. She wants to play, too."

"But look what Miriam did to my farm," said Andrew. He was ready to cry. "I can not play with my farm when Miriam is on the floor."

Mother thought a little. Then she said, "Give Miriam a few animals, Andrew. Let her play with just a few of your toys. She can play with them on the floor. You can put your barn and the other toys on the table. Miriam can not get it there."

Andrew obeyed. He said, "I have so many cows. Miriam may have a few of them. She may have a horse and a pig, too."

Soon Miriam was playing with a few of the toy animals. She sat on the floor to play with them.

Andrew put his barn and all the other animals on the table. He had a nice farm there. Andrew was very happy now. Miriam was happy, too.

HAPPY TIMES IN SPRING

Teacher Dan's Surprise

It was not winter now. It was spring. There was no snow on the ground. The days were getting warmer and warmer.

No birds came to the bird feeder. One day Dad took the feeder down and put it away.

"The birds can find food in the fields now," he said. "Next winter when it snows, we will put the feeder up again."

Peter and Levi were still going to school. One morning Teacher Dan said, "I have a surprise for the boys and girls in the first four grades. I will tell you about the surprise tonight before you go home."

The children looked at each other and smiled. They liked surprises. "What is the surprise?" they asked. "We do not want to wait until tonight. We want to know it now."

Teacher Dan just smiled. He would not tell what the surprise was. The children had to wait.

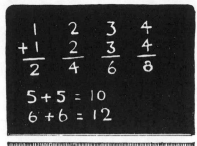

Before the children went home
that day, Teacher Dan said, "On
Friday of this week we are going
to have Pet Day at school. Every
boy and girl in the first four
grades may bring a pet to school
that day."

"Oh, oh, oh!" cried the
children. "We will like that. We
will like having Pet Day at school."
They were very, very excited.

As Peter and Levi were walking home, Peter asked, "What are you going to bring to school on Friday?"

"I will take Prince," said Levi. "I will take my little wagon, too. I want the other children to see Prince pull my wagon."

"I will take Rover to school on Friday," said Peter. "He can not pull my wagon, but he can shake hands. That will be funny when he shakes hands with all the children in school."

"Yes, it will," said Levi. "Rover will bark at all the other animals. That will be funny, too."

"Rover does not bark at other animals any more," said Peter. "He did when he was a puppy. But he knows better now. He just barks at the cows when we tell him to."

"Pet day at school will be fun," said Levi. "Friday will be an exciting day at school."

That night Peter told his family about Pet Day. Dad and Mother laughed when they heard about it.

"What will you take to school?" asked Rachel.

"I will take Rover," said Peter. "He can shake hands with all the children. Levi is going to take his dog to school, too."

Dad looked at Peter. "There will be many dogs at school on Friday," he said. "Why not take the little twin goats we have in the barn? No other boy or girl will bring twin goats to school."

Peter thought a little. Then he said, "Yes, I want to take the little goats to school. The other boys and girls will like them."

An Exciting Day

Peter did not tell the other children what he was going to bring on Pet Day. "My pets will be a surprise," he said. "You will have to wait and see them."

All week the children talked and talked about Pet Day. They could not wait until Friday.

At last it was the day before
Friday. Teacher Dan said, "If
it rains tomorrow, we can not
have our Pet Day. Then we will
have to wait until next Friday."

"I hope it will not rain," said
Peter. "I hope we can have Pet
Day tomorrow."

"I hope so, too," said Teacher
Dan. "If it does not rain
tomorrow morning, we will look
for you and your pets. Bring
food for your pets, too. They
will get hungry if they are in
school all day."

The next morning it was not
raining. The sun was out and it
was a nice day. When Peter and
Levi went to school, Prince went,
too. Levi was pulling the little
wagon.

"Where is your pet, Peter?"
asked Levi.

"My pets will not come until
noon," said Peter. "They have to
stay with their mother this
morning. That is why they could
not come with me. Dad will
bring them to school at noon."

"I guess your pets will be the little kittens you have," said Levi.

"No, no, not kittens," laughed Peter. "You will have to wait and see. I will not tell you now."

When Peter and Levi came to school, they walked around and looked at all the animals. There were big cats and little kittens. There were big dogs and little puppies. One boy had a pet squirrel in a pen. Another boy had two pet birds. A girl had a little lamb. There was one pen with six baby ducks. Another pen had a chicken with five little babies.

Teacher Dan came out of the schoolhouse. He looked at all the animals. "My, my," he said. "I think we have all the farm animals but a horse and a cow."

"Oh, no," said Peter. "My pets are not here. They will come at noon. There is no other pet here like the ones I will have."

"I guess you are going to bring a pet pig," said one boy.

"No, no, not a pig," laughed
Peter. "You will have to wait and
see. But I will tell you this much.
It is not a pet pig."

It was time for the bell. All
the animals had to go back into
their pens. The dogs were tied
to the fence. Then all the
children ran into the schoolhouse.

The boys and girls could not do good work that morning. They were all thinking about their pets.

At noon Dad came to school. He had a big box on the buggy. There were little holes in the box.

All the children came running when they saw the big box. Peter opened it. Up came one little goat's head. Then out of the box it jumped. The children laughed and laughed. "We like your pet," they said.

Then up out of the box came another goat's head. The children laughed again. "Two little goats! Two little goats!" they cried. They were very excited.

The children watched the little
goats play with each other. They
watched Prince pull the little
wagon. They played with all the
other pets, too. What fun
everyone had!

The Best Pet of All

Teacher Dan said, "I like all your pets, boys and girls. You like the pets, too. You can have fun playing with them. But the best pet of all is still coming. It will be here soon."

"What is it? What is it?" asked all the boys and girls.

"Wait and see," laughed Teacher Dan. "You will know soon. But right now the animals want something to eat. I hope you have food for your animals."

"We do," said the children.
They ran to feed their pets. Then
they watched the animals eat.

The little lamb got a bottle.
How the children all laughed to see
that lamb take the bottle.

All the boys and girls stood and
watched the lamb. No one looked
up. No one saw a man and a
donkey come walking up the road.

The man walked right up to the children before they saw him. "Hello, there!" said the man.

Everyone looked around in a hurry. Who did they see? There stood Mr. Brown and Shag.

"Oh, oh, oh!" said Peter. "Shag came to school. I am glad to see him. I have not seen that donkey for a long, long time."

"No, you have not seen Shag in the field for a long, long time," said Mr. Brown. "He had to stay in the barn all winter. He can go out into the field now, but he is in the field on the other side of the barn. You can not see him on your way to school."

"Why did you come to school today?" asked Levi. "How did you know this was Pet Day?"

"Your teacher asked me to come," said Mr. Brown. "And I wanted to come, too. I wanted you to see my pet."

"We are glad you came," said
Teacher Dan. "Do you think
Shag would want to give the boys
and girls rides?"

"I think so," said Mr. Brown.
"That is why we came. Shag has
a ride for every boy and girl who
wants one."

So all the little boys and girls
had a ride on Shag's back. Then
the big boys had a ride, too. The
big girls did not have a ride.
They did not want to ride a donkey.

By and by it was time to go
home. Mr. Brown and Shag
started down the road.

"Thank you for the rides!" said
all the boys and girls. "Good-by,
Mr. Brown. We like your pet
best of all."

The children got ready to go
home, too. Peter put the box on
Levi's wagon. Then he put the
twin goats into the box.

"Here we go," said Peter. He
started to pull the wagon.

Just then the box opened. Out
jumped a baby goat. It started to
run away.

Teacher Dan came to help the boys. "I have just what you need," he said. "I will tie the box for you. Then your goats can not jump out."

Soon the boys were on their way again. "Pet Day is the best day of all the year," said Levi.

"Yes, it is," said Peter. "It is the very best day of all."

Good-by, Grade One

It was a pretty day in spring. Peter and Levi were very happy. "Today is the last day of school," said Peter. "Tomorrow we will not go to school."

"I like school, but I want to stay home now," said Levi. "It will soon be summer. Dad will need me to help on the farm."

Soon Peter and Levi were in
school. When they heard the bell,
they ran into the schoolhouse.
They sat in their seats.

The children in Grade One did
not have much work today. They
were done with all their books.
Teacher Dan gave them a picture
to color.

Soon Teacher Dan said, "We
want to talk about what you will do
this summer. What do you think
you will do, Peter?"

"I will help Dad work on the
farm," said Peter. "I will play
with Rachel and Andrew and
Miriam, too."

Up went Levi's hand. "I will
go play with Peter on some days, "
he said. "Peter and I will have
good times playing with each
other. "

A little girl said, "I will help
Mother work. I will play with our
baby, too. "

Another girl said, "I will go to Grandfather's house. Grandfather and Grandmother live far, far away. Our family will go see them this summer. We will stay a week."

Teacher Dan said, "I think you will all have a good time this summer. You can have a very good time by working and playing with the others in your family."

Soon it was time for the boys and girls to go home. Teacher Dan stood at the door and watched them go.

"Good-by, Teacher Dan," said
the boys and girls.

"Good-by, good-by," said
Teacher Dan. "Have a good time
this summer. I hope to see you
again next year."

"I will try and come back next
year," said Peter. "But I will not
be in Grade One then. I will be in
Grade Two."

"Yes, you will," laughed
Teacher Dan. "I will see you in
Grade Two next year."

Word List

5. six
   years
6. birthday
   late
   tell
7.
8. smiled
   very
   cold
   cap
9.
10.
11. obey
12. Grandfather
    Grandmother
13.
14. buggy
15. surprise
16.
17. open
18.
19. cake
20. everyone
    some
21. afternoon
    there
22.
23. who
24.
25. myself
26.

27.
28.
29. any
30.
31. yourself
32.
33.
34. sun
35. last
36. another
37. asked
38. chair
    herself
39.
40.
41. our
42. anyone
    anything
43.
44. glad
45. grade
46. pretty
    sky
47. hat
    Mr.
    lived
    himself
    gray
    ears
48.

49. head
    tail
    hee-haw
50. schoolhouse
    about
    donkey
51. told
52. bell
    thinking
53. seat
    teacher
    Dan
    forget
54. knew
55. took
    room
56.
57. face
    book
58. sit
    picture
    color
59. cow
60. done
    children
61.
62.
63.
64. thought
65.

66. hope	91. before	114. maybe
dinner	92. deep	tomorrow
bucket	snowman	wait
apple	kitchen	115.
bite	93.	116. fly
67.	94. breakfast	117. until
68. seen	95. mittens	118. fell
69. hurry	96. family	119.
70. Shag	snowball	120. squirrel
week	rolled	121. far
every	top	122.
71. friend	97. eyes	123. food
72. someday	nose	124. toy
73.	98. mouth	sheep
74. talked	99. fun	chickens
75.	four	125.
76. corn	100.	126. pen
77. carry	101.	127. blocks
78. calf	102. letter	128.
twins	103.	129.
79.	104. warm	130. shop
80.	melt	wood
81.	105.	hammer
82. forgot	106. church	paint
83.	107.	131.
84. their	108. happened	132.
85.	109.	133.
86.	110. bird	134. wet
87. would	111. ground	dry
88.	hungry	135. floor
89. winter	112. feeder	136.
90. snowed	watch	137.
long	feed	138.
early	113. seeds	139.

140. few
141. spring
142. warmer
143. each
144. Friday
     pet
     bring
     excited
145. shake
146. better
147. why
148. exciting
149.
150. noon
151. lamb
     five
152.
153. tied
154.
155.
156. best
157. bottle
158.
159.
160.
161.
162.
163. summer
164.
165.
166.
167.